Contents

OXFORD
UNIVERSITY PRESS

Great Clarendon Street, Oxford, OX2 6DP, United Kingdom

Oxford University Press is a department of the University
of Oxford. It furthers the University's objective of excellence
in research, scholarship, and education by publishing
worldwide. Oxford is a registered trade mark of Oxford
University Press in the UK and in certain other countries

Text © Julia Donaldson 2006 and 2007

The Trunk and the Skunk illustrations © Woody 2006
The Scrap Rocket illustrations © Jonathan Allen 2006
Ron Rabbit's Big Day illustrations © Jonathan Allen 2007
The Wishing Elf illustrations © Anni Axworthy 2007
Bob Bug and the Insect Club illustrations © Deborah Allwright 2007
Where is the Snail? illustrations © Kay Widdowson 2007

All other illustrations © Oxford University Press 2006

The moral rights of the author have been asserted

This edition first published 2018

British Library Cataloguing in Publication Data
Data available

ISBN: 978-0-19-276479-9

10 9 8 7 6 5 4 3

Paper used in the production of this book is a natural, recyclable product
made from wood grown in sustainable forests. The manufacturing process
conforms to the environmental regulations of the country of origin.

Printed in Great Britain by Bell and Bain Ltd, Glasgow

Acknowledgements

Series Editor: Clare Kirtley

Cover illustration by Woody

Gran is Cross illustrated by Ross Collins

Gran is Cross

Tips for reading Gran is Cross together

This story practises blending groups of consonants at the beginning of words. Look out for these in the story:

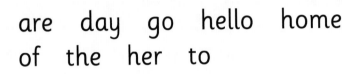

twins **Gr**an **fl**ick **br**ings **pr**am **fr**og
steps **bl**ack **Sp**ot **sn**ack **dr**ink **cl**oth
cross **gl**ad **sm**ash

Your child might find these words tricky:

are day go hello home
of the her to

These words are common, but your child may not have learned how to sound them out yet. Say the words for your child if they do not know them.

Before you begin, ask your child to read the title by sounding out first (saying each sound out loud, e.g. *cr-o-ss*) and then blending the word together (e.g. *cross*), as much as possible. Look at the picture together. What do you think this story is about?

Remind your child to read unfamiliar words by saying the individual sounds separately and then blending them together quickly to read the word. When you have finished reading, look through the story again and:

- Talk about how the characters are feeling by the end of the story. Ask your child, *Why do you think Gran was cross?*

- Encourage your child to find words in the story that start with the letters *fr* (*frog, Fred*). Try to write the words. Say all of the sounds in the word separately then write the letter that makes each sound.

The twins go to visit Gran.

Flick brings a pram. Fred brings his frog.

Gran is on the steps.

Hello, Gran.

Gran has a black cat.

9

Gran gets the twins a snack.

Flick spills her drink on the cloth. Gran is cross.

Fred drops his sandwich in the pram. Gran is cross.

But Spot the cat is glad.

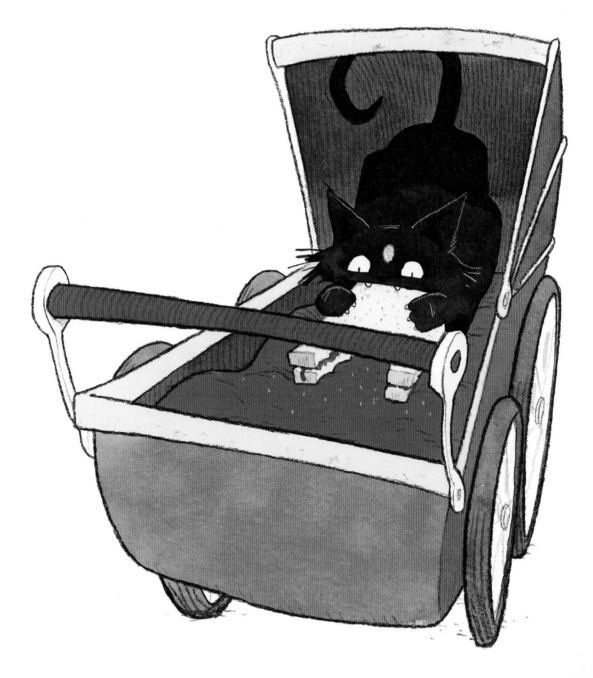

The frog jumps in the jam.
Fred grabs him.

Smash!
Gran is cross.

The frog jumps and jumps.
Spot runs and runs.

The frog jumps on the clock.
Gran is cross.

At the end of the day the twins
go home.

Gran is glad. The twins are glad.

But Spot is sad.

The Trunk and the Skunk

Tips for reading The Trunk and the Skunk together

This story practises blending groups of consonants at the beginning and/or end of words. Look out for these in the story:

stamp tu**sks** **tr**u**nk** **l**i**ft** **dr**i**nk** **sl**osh **sm**ell **sn**iff **sk**u**nk**

Your child might find these words tricky:

bananas good have I my
no of oh the

These words are common, but your child may not have learned how to sound them out yet. Say the words for your child if they do not know them.

Before you begin, ask your child to read the title by sounding out first (saying each sound out loud, e.g. *tr-u-nk*) and then blending the word together (e.g. *trunk*), as much as possible. Look at the picture together. What do you think this story is about?

Remind your child to read unfamiliar words by saying the individual sounds separately and then blending them together quickly to read the word. When you have finished reading, look through the story again and:

- Talk about what a mammoth can do with its trunk. Ask your child, *What would you do if you had a trunk?*
- Encourage your child to find two words on page 24 that rhyme (*stamp* and *tramp*). Can they think of other words that rhyme with *stamp? (lamp, damp, camp)*

I am a mammoth.

I have big, thick legs. I can stamp on things.

Stamp, tramp, crash!

24

I have long tusks. I can dig with them.

And I have a long trunk.

I can do lots of things with my trunk.

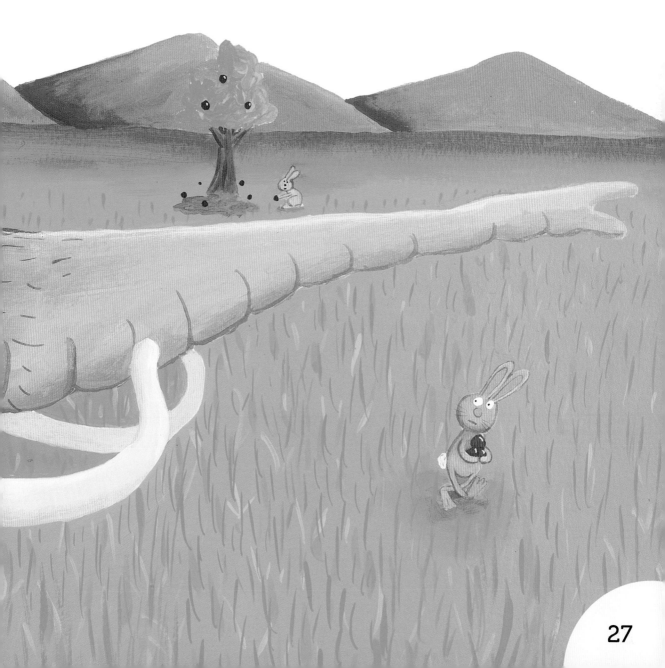

I can pick things up.

I can lift things.

I can drink.

I can slosh my mum and dad!

Stop that!

And I can smell things with my trunk.

I can smell *good* things...
Sniff, sniff! Bananas!

And I can smell *bad* things...
Sniff, sniff! A skunk!

This skunk stinks! I will slosh him!

Slosh! That will get rid of the smell.

Sniff, sniff…

Oh no! The skunk still smells
of skunk.

The Scrap Rocket

Tips for reading The Scrap Rocket together

This story practises blending groups of consonants at the beginning and/or end of words. Look out for these in the story:

colle**ct**s **scr**ap **and** **pl**ank pu**mp**
spring **str**ap **cl**ink **tw**ist **thr**ill
splash

Your child might find this word tricky:

submarine

Explain that we can read longer words by breaking them up into bits. Say the word for your child if they do not know it and explain what it means.

Before you begin, ask your child to read the title by sounding out first (saying each sound out loud, e.g. *scr-a-p*) and then blending the word together (e.g. *scrap*), as much as possible. Look at the picture together. What do you think this story is about?

Remind your child to read unfamiliar words by saying the individual sounds separately and then blending them together quickly to read the word. When you have finished reading, look through the story again and:

- Talk about what Ron Rabbit collected and why. Ask your child, *What would you like to make out of scrap things?*

- Encourage your child to find two words on pages 46 and 47 of the story that rhyme (*spring, string*). Which letters create the rhyme? Can you think of other words that rhyme with *spring*? (*sing, bring, sting, swing, thing, wing, king, ring*)

Ron Rabbit is collecting things.

Ron collects a tin,

a tap,

a pot and

a lid.

Ron collects a plug,

a plank and

a pump.

Next, Ron collects a spring,

a strap and

lots of string.

48

49

It's a rocket!

Lift-off!

But then...

Splash!

It's not a rocket.

It's a submarine!

Ron Rabbit's Big Day

Tips for reading Ron Rabbit's Big Day together

This story practises this letter pattern:

ee

Ask your child to point to this letter pattern and say the sound (*ee* as in *need*). Look out for this letter pattern in the story.

Your child might find these words tricky:

of to the no he one two new bottle for have they after are was she says all her about Mr Mrs

These words are common, but your child may not be able to sound them out yet. Say the words for your child if they do not know them.

Before you begin, ask your child to read the title by sounding out first (saying each letter out loud, e.g. *b-i-g*) and then blending the word together (e.g. *big*), as much as possible. Look at the picture together. What do you think the story is about?

Remind your child to read unfamiliar words by saying the individual sounds separately and then blending them together quickly to read the word. When you have finished reading the story, look through it again and:

- Ask your child, *Why did Ron trip the man up?* (He was stealing things from Mr Preston.)

- Point to the letter pattern that makes the long vowel sound in *creeping*. Say what sound this letter pattern makes (*ee*). Find and read some more words in the story that contain the letter pattern *ee* (*needs, three, need, sees, green, asleep*).

58

Ron Rabbit has a new job. He is a milkman.

Ron has to get up at six. The sun is not up yet.

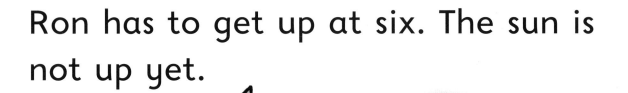

Ron fills his van with milk. Then he sets off.

clink clink

Mrs Jessop needs one bottle of milk. Ron dumps it on the step.

Two bottles for Miss Quin. Three bottles for Mr Chang.

Mr and Mrs Preston have ten children. They need ten bottles of milk!

Ron is getting the bottles from his van when he sees a man. The man is creeping along.

Is it Mr Preston? No, this man is not as thin, and he has a big black sack on his back.

When the man sees Ron he runs. "Stop!" yells Ron. He runs after the man.

Ron trips the man up. The man drops the sack and Ron grabs it. The man runs off.

In the sack are lots of things …
a clock, a pink jug, a big cup,
a green lamp, and a cash box!

Ron rings the bell. Mrs Preston is cross. "I was asleep, Ron," she says.

But then she sees all the things, and Ron tells her about the bad man. "Thank you, Ron!" says Mrs Preston.

Mr Preston rings the cops.

The cops catch the bad man.

Ron gets a medal.

The Wishing Elf

Tips for reading The Wishing Elf together

This story practises this letter pattern:

ie

Ask your child to point to this letter pattern and say the sound (*ie* as in *tie*). Look out for this letter pattern in the story.

Your child might find these words tricky:

I   to   the   of   come   school   he   you   all
one   says   was   for   everyone   now   have
another   your   what   do

These words are common, but your child may not be able to sound them out yet. Say the words for your child if they do not know them.

Before you begin, ask your child to read the title. Remind your child to read words they do not recognise by sounding out first (saying each letter out loud, e.g. *e-l-f*) and then blending the word together (e.g. *elf*). Look at the picture together. What do you think this story is about?

Remind your child to read unfamiliar words by saying the individual sounds separately and then blending them together quickly to read the word. When you have finished reading the story, look through it again and:

- Ask your child, *Why did Miss Smith wish for an extra hand?* (She had lots of things to do.)

- Find and read two words on page 85 that rhyme (*tries*, *flies*). Point to the letter pattern that makes the long vowel sound in these words. Say what sound this letter pattern makes (*ie*). Point to the beginning two letters in each word. Say each sound they make. Think of other words that begin with the two sounds *fl* or *tr* (e.g. *flag, flap, fly, trip, trap, tree*).

An elf has come to school! He is standing on Miss Smith's desk. "You can all have one wish," he says.

"I wish I had a parrot," says Dan.

The elf claps his hands. "Abracadabra!" he says. The next second, a parrot flies in!

"I wish I was rich," says Kevin.

"I wish I had wings," says Yasmin.

Meg wishes for a big pie and
lots of chips.

Majid wishes for a forest!

"I wish I had a dragon," says Gwen.

A dragon flies in. It tries to get the parrot. Miss Smith has to tie it up.

"I wish I sat next to Patrick," says Ross.

But then Patrick says, "I wish
I sat next to Callum."

Everyone gets a wish.

"Now Miss Smith must have a wish," says the elf. Miss Smith thinks. "I wish I had an extra hand!" she says.

The next second, Miss Smith has an extra hand. "Now I can do lots of things," she says.

"I must visit another school now," says the elf.

If the elf visits your school, what will you wish for?

Bob Bug
and the
Insect Club

Tips for reading Bob Bug and the Insect Club together

This story practises this letter pattern:

oa

Ask your child to point to this letter pattern and say the sound (*oa* as in *toad*). Look out for this letter pattern in the story.

Your child might find these words tricky:

to   the   I   no   you   says   for   he   come
be   some   have   are   he's   like   eat   can't
they   gives   some   I'm   hungry

These words are common, but your child may not be able to sound them out yet. Say the words for your child if they do not know them.

Before you begin, ask your child to read the title. Remind your child to read words they do not recognise by sounding out first (saying each letter out loud, e.g. *B-o-b*) and then blending the word together (e.g. *Bob*). Look at the picture together. What do you think this story is about?

Remind your child to read unfamiliar words by saying the individual sounds separately and then blending them together quickly to read the word. When you have finished reading the story, look through it again and:

- Ask your child, *Why wasn't Bob hungry?* (He had eaten toast, nuts and buns in his Club for Insects.)

- Point to the letter pattern that makes the long vowel sound in *cockroach*. Say what sound this letter pattern makes (*oa*). Find and read some more words in the book that contain the letter pattern *oa* (*toast, toad, toads, roast*).

94

Bob Bug and his mum are in the kitchen. Bob has a pen and a pad.

"Can you spell 'insects'?" says Bob.
"Yes," says Mum.

Bob sticks this on his den:
"Club for Insects".

Bob is sitting in his den. Ant taps on the den. "I am an insect," he says. "Can I come in?"

"Yes," says Bob. "You can be in the club."

Ant brings some toast. "Thank you," says Bob. Ant and Bob sit in the den and munch the toast.

Then Moth taps on the den.
"Can I come in?" she says.
"Have you got six legs?" says Bob.
"Yes, I have. I am an insect,"
says Moth.

Tap, tap, tap!

Moth brings some nuts. Bob and Ant and Moth sit in the den and crunch the nuts.

Then Toad taps on the den.
"Can I be in the club?" he says.

"Are you an insect, Toad?" says Bob. "No, he's not!" says Ant. "Toads like to EAT insects," says Moth.

"Then you can't come in,"
Bob tells Toad.

Cockroach taps on Bob's den.
He brings a drink and ten buns.
"Yum yum," says Bob. They eat
the buns and sip the drink.

Then Mum Bug yells,
"Bob! Come in!"

Mum gives Bob some roast chicken.

"Eat up, Bob," she says.

"I'm not hungry," says Bob.

Where is the Snail?

Tips for reading Where is the Snail? together

This story practises this letter pattern:

ai

Ask your child to point to this letter pattern and say the sound (*ai* as in *snail*). Look out for this letter pattern in the story.

Your child might find these words tricky:

the flamingo one you after
her are octopus how many

These words are common, but your child may not be able to sound them out yet. Say the words for your child if they do not know them.

Before you begin, ask your child to read the title. Remind your child to read words they do not recognise by sounding out first (saying each sound out loud, e.g. *sn-ai-l*) and then blending the word together (e.g. *snail*). Look at the picture together. What do you think this story is about?

Remind your child to read unfamiliar words by saying the individual sounds separately and then blending them together quickly to read the word. When you have finished reading the story, look through it again and:

- Ask your child, *Which animals are awake at night?* (The bat and the fox.)

- Find and read two words on pages 126 and 127 that rhyme (*tail, snail*). Point to the letter pattern that makes the long vowel sound in each word. Say what sound this letter pattern makes (*ai*). Find and read some more words in the book that contain the letter pattern *ai* (*sails, wait*).

A red parrot flaps its wings.
A chimp swings.
A pink flamingo stands on one leg.
But can you see the snail?

Hens cluck.
Ducks quack.

A black cat sits in the sun.
But can you see the snail?

A squirrel cracks a nut.
A thrush sings in its nest.

A web hangs from a twig.
But can you see the snail?

A boat sails.
A gull pecks at a sandwich.

A crab runs across a rock.
But can you see the snail?

A frog jumps.
A duck swims across the pond.

Seven ducklings swim after her.
But can you see the snail?

Bees buzz.
A man digs.

A robin sits on a twig.
But can you see the snail?

Bats flit.
A fox hunts.

124

In the street, the lamps are lit.
But can you see the snail?

125

A cat licks her kittens.
A dog wags his tail.

A rabbit munches a carrot.
But can you see the snail?

Six pink fish swim along.
A big black fish snaps at them.
An octopus lies in wait.
How many snails can you see?